Why Raven Is Black

retold by Jay Parker
illustrated by Marjory Gardner

Harcourt
SCHOOL PUBLISHERS

Printed in the United States of America

ISBN 10: 0-15-350406-4
ISBN 13: 978-0-15-350406-8

Ordering Options
ISBN 10: 0-15-350332-7 (Grade 2 Below-Level Collection)
ISBN 13: 978-0-15-350332-0 (Grade 2 Below-Level Collection)
ISBN 10: 0-15-357433-X (package of 5)
ISBN 13: 978-0-15-357433-7 (package of 5)

1 2 3 4 5 6 7 8 9 10   179   15 14 13 12 11 10 09 08 07 06

Long ago, birds were all
the color gray. One day, with
a little paint, they changed
that.

Goose knew Raven was very
clever. "Come and join me,
Raven," Goose said.

"I would like a nice black and white pattern," said Goose. Raven painted it well.

Goose liked the pattern that
Raven had painted.
"Please paint me the same,"
said Raven.

Goose started to paint.
"Don't paint that feather!"
exclaimed Raven.

Goose kept on painting.
"I didn't paint that way!" cried
Raven.

"Raven, you must accept the way I do it," Goose said.

Goose had painted almost
half of her friend.
Then Raven said, "I'm tired of
waiting."

Goose threw down the brush.
"You are not being fair!" Goose
cried. "You may be clever, but
you are too impatient!"

Goose dumped the black paint
all over Raven and left.

Raven did not give up though.
He asked the other birds to
help him.

It was clear to them that
Raven would not change.
That is why Raven is still black
all over.

Think Critically

1. In the story, what color were all birds long ago?

2. What were the most important things that happened in the story?

3. Why did Goose dump black paint all over Raven?

4. How do you know that this is not a true story?

5. Would you change the ending of the story? How?

 Language Arts

Write a Story Write a story telling how you think the peacock got its colorful feathers.

 **School-Home Connection** Talk about *Why Raven Is Black* with a family member. Then talk about ways Raven and Goose could have worked together better.

Word Count: 174